Disney · PIXAR

THE INCREDIBLES

Disney · PIXAR

FINDING NEMO

Disney · PIXAR

MONSTERS, INC.

Featuring your favourite *Disney · PIXAR* films!

EGMONT
We bring stories to life

First published in Great Britain 2009
by Egmont UK Limited
239 Kensington High Street, London W8 6SA

Editor: Jaine Keskeys
Art Editor: Phil Williams

Note to parents: adult supervision is recommended when sharp-pointed items,
such as scissors, are in use.

ISBN 978 1 4052 4671 2
1 3 5 7 9 10 8 6 4 2
Printed in Italy

This Annual belongs to

Name:

....

Age:

....

My favourite character is:

....

Disney ANNUAL 2010

Featuring your favourite *Disney* · PIXAR *films!*

THE INCREDIBLES

The lost hat

1 One sunny day, Andy was playing in his sandpit with his two favourite toys. "I'm going to bury you in this alien quicksand!" he told Woody.

2 "Don't worry, Woody, Buzz will save you!" cried Andy. He then made Buzz swoop over the sand, like it was the surface of an alien planet.

3 It was soon tea time and Andy's mum called him inside. "Buzz, my hat's still in the sandpit," Woody whispered, as Andy carried them both back to the house.

4 Back in Andy's room, Woody began to panic. "I can't be a sheriff without my sheriff's hat!" he cried. "Don't worry, we'll get it back," Buzz told his friend.

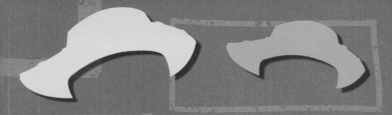

5 When Andy was asleep that night, the two brave toys sneaked out of the window and back to the sandpit. "Sssh!" Woody warned the other toys.

6 "OK, let's find that hat," Buzz said, when they reached the sandpit. But it was so dark that they couldn't see anything. "This is hopeless!" Woody cried.

7 "Don't worry, my laser will aid us in our search!" Buzz said, grandly. He pressed a button on his arm and lit up the sandpit. "Great idea!" Woody laughed.

8 Using the light from his toy laser, Buzz quickly found Woody's hat. "Your sheriff is back in town!" Woody cheered, as Buzz held up the hat.

9 Buzz and Woody hurried back to Andy's bedroom. Woody couldn't wait to put his hat back on. But when he did, a shower of sand fell onto his head!

10 "Puffft!" Woody spluttered. The toys all laughed. "Well, I think we'll have to call you the Sandy Sheriff from now on, Woody!" Buzz giggled.

The end

About the story

1 Where was Andy playing?

2 What did Woody lose?

3 Who lit up the sandpit?

4 What happened when Woody put his hat back on?

Answers: 1) in his sandpit. 2) his hat. 3) Buzz. 4) a shower of sand fell onto his head!

Space sketch

Etch has sketched a space scene to make Buzz feel at home! Can you add some cool colours to the picture below?

How many eyes does the Alien have?

A big bounce

The toys are bouncing on Andy's bed! Can you put them in order, starting with the one who has bounced the highest? We've done the first one for you!

1

12

Picnic puzzle

The toys are enjoying a picnic! Can you spot five differences in the bottom picture?

13

Defeat Zurg

Buzz must cross the floating disks to defeat Zurg and he needs your help!

How to play

You will need: A dice and a counter for each player.
Place all the counters on the **Start** disk and then take it in turns to roll the dice. Move along the path of floating disks towards Zurg, the same number of disks as the number thrown. Players can only land on the **Finish** disk if they get the exact number on their last throw. For example, if you are on disk 12, you must throw a 4 to land on the Finish disk, or wait until your next turn. The first player to reach Zurg, wins!

The space portal

It's no fun for the toys when Rex decides he can't play with them. Can they find a way to bring their dinosaur buddy back?

One day, Rex and Hamm were reading Andy's Big Dinosaur Book. Rex loved looking at the pictures. Some of the dinosaurs looked like him! "Look at this one," Rex laughed. "He's green with lots of teeth, too!"

Hamm looked at the words that were written next to the picture. "Dinosaurs lived a long time ago," he read. "No one has ever seen a living dinosaur."

Rex quickly looked through the book but he couldn't find any pictures of people with dinosaurs. "Hamm must be right," he thought.

Later, when all the toys gathered to play, Rex was still looking at Andy's

book. "Hey, Rex," Woody shouted, "it's playtime. Come and join us!"

"No thanks, Woody," Rex replied, sadly. "Dinosaurs can't play with cowboys or any toys."

"Don't be silly," Woody told him, "it's more fun when everyone joins in."

"I'm sorry, I can't," Rex said, showing Woody the dinosaur book. "It says here that dinosaurs lived many years ago, even before people, so no one ever played with them. So, I can't play with you any more."

Rex then took the book under Andy's bed so that he couldn't see the other toys playing without him.

The other toys weren't happy. "Our games won't be the same without Rex!" Jessie said, sadly. "We must find a way to bring our friend back."

They needed a plan! So, everyone thought about what they could do. "I know a way that Rex can play with us again," Buzz said, finally, "but I'll need everyone's help!"

The toys all helped Buzz to pile the building blocks and some empty boxes into a big, square shape. "It looks like a door!" Jessie laughed.

"That's right. We've built a space portal. If there's one thing every space ranger knows, it's that anything could appear from a space portal!" Buzz explained to the toys.

"Even a dinosaur?" Rex asked, peeking out from under Andy's bed.

When Buzz nodded, Rex ran across the floor and leapt through the space portal. "That means that I can play with you guys, after all," he said, with a big smile on his face. Everyone cheered. Hamm smiled at Rex. "It wouldn't be any fun without you, pal," he said.

The end

Colouring book

Rex is busy reading his book! Get busy with your pens and colour in this picture of him.

Who is on the cover of Rex's book? Tick the correct box.

Woody   or   Zurg

18

Answer: Zurg.

Tangled beads

Jessie is in a bit of a tangle! Which string of beads will lead her to Woody?

How many green beads can you count on the page? Write your answer in the box.

Dance partner

1 One day, WALL·E was busy tidying up planet Earth, when he came across a big mirror. But, of course, WALL·E didn't realise that it was a mirror.

2 Looking into the mirror, WALL·E was so excited to see another robot on Earth! He waved to it and at that same moment, the robot waved back at him!

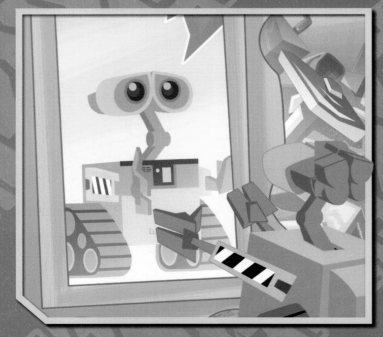

3 WALL·E wondered if the new robot could dance. WALL·E really loved to dance! So, he put down his pile of trash and decided to find out.

4 WALL·E was soon showing the robot all of his best dance moves. WALL·E was amazed when the robot knew all of the moves, too!

5 But WALL·E felt that something was missing... The two robots needed some music to dance to! Then WALL·E had an idea.

6 WALL·E motioned to the other robot to wait and then he set off. He searched through piles and piles of rubbish, collecting the things that he needed.

7 WALL·E used the rubbish that he had collected to make a string of wind chimes. "Clang! Bong! Bang!" the metal pipes sang as they crashed together.

8 Now the two robots had music, they could dance all day. The new robot copied WALL·E's every move and WALL·E felt he had found a great dance partner!

The end

WALL·E's words

WALL·E has followed EVE into space! What four space words can you find in this wheel?

Flying colours

EVE is giving WALL-E a lift! Help her by giving them both some uplifting colours.

What colour are EVE's eyes? Colour the box the same colour.

23

Colourful cubes

WALL·E and EVE have each built a tower of trash cubes!
Who will colour all of their cubes first in this fun game?

How to play

You will need: A dice and coloured pens.

This is a game for two players. Decide who will be WALL·E and who will be EVE. Take it in turns to throw the dice and colour in a cube from your tower that matches the number thrown. Miss a go if you have already coloured all of the cubes that match the number thrown. The first player to colour all of their cubes, wins!

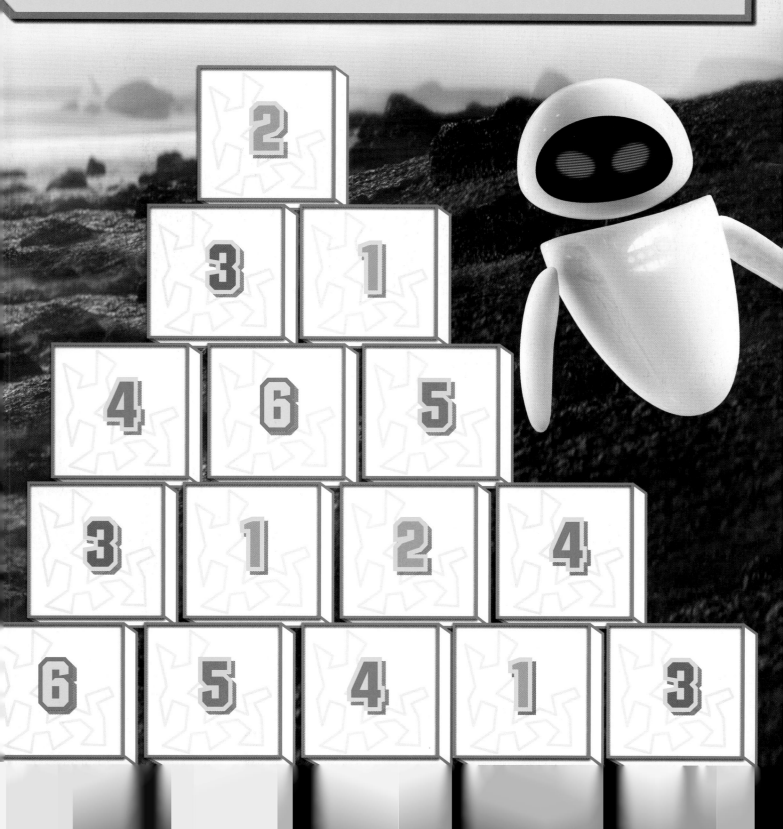

Planet Earth puzzles

EVE has arrived on planet Earth. Solve these puzzles while WALL·E shows her around!

1 What word is written on the cubes?

2 How many wheels like this one can you count?

3 What is WALL·E holding?

r
u
b
b
i
s
h

WALL·E

Answers: 1) rubbish. 2) 5. 3) a plant.

4 Brighten up WALL·E's home with some colour!

Can you spot these objects in the scene? Tick the boxes as you spot each one.

27

WALL·E at work

While WALL·E is busy cleaning up the Earth,
you can get busy by giving him some colour!

How many screws can you spot in the scene? Write your answer in the box.

Answer: 9.

Correct colours

EVE is having fun with this tricky coloured cube! Can you see which panel matches EVE's cube? Tick the correct box.

Monster truck

1 One day, Sally raced over to Lightning. "I just saw a monster truck!" she cried. "There are no monster trucks in Radiator Springs, Sally!" Lightning laughed.

2 Just then, Sheriff came speeding towards them. "What a day I've had! A monster truck chased me and I barely got away!" Sheriff wailed.

3 Suddenly, Lightning saw a giant car coming into town. "Oh no! I think it IS a monster truck!" Lightning cried. They all drove away in different directions.

4 "I'll get you, little red car!" the monster truck shouted, chasing after Lightning. "I am speed, you can't get me!" Lightning shouted back, driving off the road.

5 Lightning had remembered Doc's lesson about how to turn on dirt. "Ka-chow!" he laughed, as he spun and kicked up dirt at the monster truck.

6 Unable to see through the dirt, the monster truck lost control and swerved. "Owww!" it cried, crashing into a cactus. Bits of truck flew everywhere!

7 Now, Lightning could see that the monster truck was actually Mater, hiding under old car parts! "Shucks, it took me ages to build that truck!" Mater cried.

8 "I'll help you to rebuild it, buddy. We'll tell everyone that the monster truck is still after us!" Lightning laughed. The friends couldn't wait to trick the townsfolk!

The end 31

Spraying stars

Ramone is brightening up Radiator Springs for his friends!
Can you spot ten star shapes in the picture he has sprayed?

Tick the box when you've spotted all ten stars!

Answers: 1 - On the left building. **2** - At the end of Mater's hook. **3** - On the building at the end of the road. **4** - On Luigi. **5** - On Guido. **6, 7 and 8** - On the front sign. **9 and 10** - On the back sign.

A helping hook

Trace over the blue line to help Mater pull up Lightning, then add some colour!

What number is written on Lightning? Write your answer in the box.

Answer: 95.

33

Cactus course

Lightning and Mater are having a race! Cheer them on with the Radiator Springs crowd and complete the questions, too.

1 Who is about to win the race, Lightning or Mater?

2 What colour are the flowers on this cactus?

3 Which two cacti look exactly the same?

☐ and ☐

Mater

Lightning

a

b

c

d

1

2   4   2

1   3

4 Colour the flags in the crowd!

e

f

5 What do the numbers in the dust cloud add up to? ☐

---

6 Which detail below is not from the scene? Tick the box!

a ☐   b ☐   c ☐   d ☐   e ☐

Drive time

Sally and Lightning are taking a drive and it has turned into a race! Who will reach the finish first?

Start
1
2
10
11
12
13
14
15
16

How to play

You will need: A dice and a counter for each player.
This is a game for two players. Decide who will be Sally and who will be Lightning. Take it in turns to throw the dice and move around the track the same number of spaces as the number thrown. If you land on a space that contains your car's shadow, have an extra turn. If you land on a space that contains the other car's shadow, miss a turn. The first player to reach the finish, is the winner!

Winning colours

Doc Hudson is back at the racing track to help Lightning McQueen win! Trace over the pale blue line and then add some colour.

Who does Doc want to win? Tick the correct box.

Chick Hicks ☐

Lightning McQueen ☐

38

Tool time

Luigi and Guido keep lots of tools in their tyre shop. Can you match the tools in the panel at the bottom to the spaces in the toolbox?

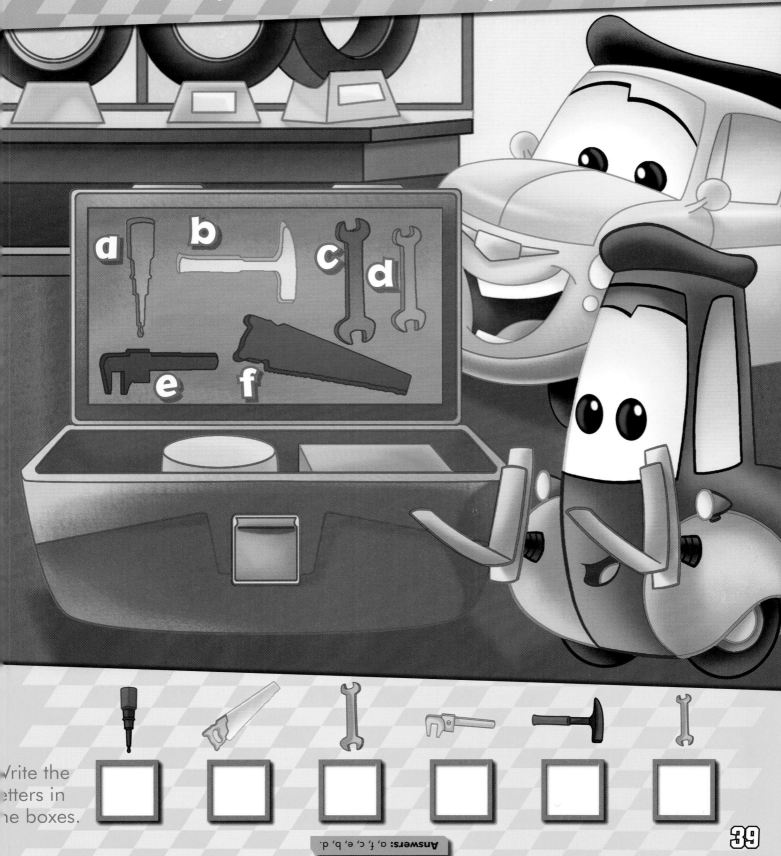

Write the letters in the boxes.

Pebble plan

(1) One day, the dentist was telling a patient all about the fish tank in his office. "I really enjoy looking at my fish while I work!" he said.

(2) The patient was interested to hear about the unique fish. "May I take a closer look at them?" the patient asked. "Sure," replied the dentist, proudly.

(3) So, when the dentist had finished, the patient peered into the fish tank. "That's a nice looking clownfish," he said, admiring Nemo's bright orange colour.

(4) Later, that night, the door to the dentist's office creaked open. The patient who had been admiring the fish earlier, crept quietly into the room.

5 Nemo woke up to see the patient holding a plastic bag filled with water. "It looks just big enough to hold a fish my size!" Nemo thought.

6 Suddenly, the patient plunged his hand into the water. "Go away!" cried Nemo, waking up the rest of the Tank Gang. "I want to stay here with my friends!"

7 Bloat, the blowfish, had an idea. "Quick, pass me a pebble!" he yelled. The Tank Gang watched as Bloat blew a pebble right into the patient's face!

8 "Ouch!" cried the patient. He quickly ran from the office, holding his jaw. Nemo and the Tank Gang were very pleased with Bloat's quick thinking!

9 The next day, the patient was back in the dentist's chair with a chipped tooth. But this time, he didn't glance once at Nemo and his friends in the tank.

10 "It looks like a small stone hit you," said the dentist. The patient didn't tell him that the small stone was a pebble from the dentist's own fish tank! *The end*

About the story

1 What did the dentist enjoy doing while he worked?

2 What type of fish is Nemo?

3 Who blew a pebble at the patient?

4 What did the pebble chip?

Answers: 1) looking at his fish. 2) a clownfish. 3) Bloat. 4) the patient's tooth.

Balloon Bloat

Make your own blowfish, just like Bloat!

You will need: Newspaper, a balloon, glue, scissors, paint, a pin, card and googly eyes.

1 Blow up a balloon and and glue on pieces of newspaper. Twist some of the pieces into spikes.

2 Repeat a few times, adding more layers. When the newspaper pieces have dried and hardened, paint them. Use a pin to pop the balloon inside.

3 Cut out fins from card and stick them on, then add some googly eyes!

Blast of colour

Give Mount Wannahockaloogie and the Tank Gang some cool colours!

How many arms does Peach, the starfish, have? Write your answer in the box.

Dory's doubles

Dory is seeing double! Can you draw lines to link the pairs of fish?

45

School trip

Mr. Ray has taken Nemo's class to see a sunken ship. Join them for some fun!

1 What are Nemo and his friends looking at?

2 Can you point to two boots?

Answers: 1) a message in a bottle. 3) a and d. 4) 6.

a b c d e

3 Which two fish look the same?

[ ] and [ ]

4 How many red jewels can you count? [ ]

5 Can you find three shells hidden in the picture? Colour a shell each time you spot one!

Making music

Nemo and his friends are playing their favourite musical instruments. Which small picture in the panel at the bottom is not from the big picture?

Tick the correct box.

a

b

c

d

Counting clams

Help Marlin through this maze to reach Nemo,
making sure you pass each clam along the way!

How many clams are
there in total? Write
your answer in the box.

Answer: 8 clams.

Monster bowl!

1 One day, Sulley was having a great scare shift at Monsters, Inc. "Look at all the screams Sulley's collected!" Mike proudly told a group of Scarers.

2 "Ummm, I don't see any scream canisters, Mike," one Scarer replied. He was right. The canisters had been taken by sneaky Randall!

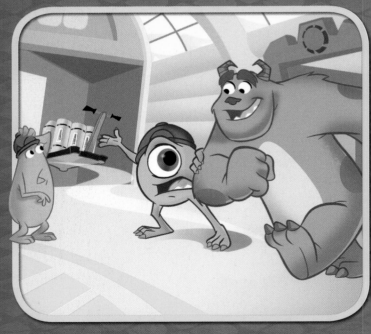

3 Mike couldn't see Randall, because his colours had blended in with the Scare Floor. "Hey!" Mike shouted, "Someone stop those runaway canisters!"

4 Just then, Sulley arrived back on the Scare Floor. "How are things going so far, Mike?" he asked. "Not so well, Sulley, our screams are escaping!" Mike cried.

5 "No problem, pal! Get ready for a fun ride," Sulley replied. He picked up Mike, just like a bowling ball. "Move out of the way, Scarers!" he laughed.

6 "Wheee!" Mike cried, as he rolled across the Scare Floor. He rolled straight into the escaping scream canisters, knocking them over like bowling pins!

7 Randall was trapped under the canisters that Mike had knocked over! "Thanks, Randall. I needed the bowling practice for the game tonight!" Sulley joked.

8 That evening, Sulley and Mike went to the Monster Bowling Alley. "Bowling is great fun," Sulley said to his friend. "Yeah, especially when I'm the ball!" Mike agreed.

The end

Scare pals

Sulley and Mike have had a good scare day!
Give them and their canisters some colour.

What colour are
Sulley's spots?
Colour the box
the same colour!

52

Help Randall hide

Randall hides by blending into the background! To help him, can you draw each pattern on to him and then add the correct colours?

Keeping fit

Sulley and Mike are at the gym! Answer these questions before they finish their workout.

1 What word is written here?

healthy

2 Can you put these bottles in size order, from largest to smallest?

a b c d e

54

3 Can you find four pairs of monster trainers?

4 How many hula hoops is Celia hula-hooping?

5 Which three treats would be healthy snacks? Tick the boxes!

55

Super delivery!

① One day, as Mr. Incredible was walking along, he noticed a big traffic jam. "I wonder what's going on?" he thought, as a crowd of people gathered.

② A lorry had broken down and it was blocking the road, causing chaos. "I'll use my super strength to help all these poor drivers," Mr. Incredible decided.

③ With his super strength, Mr. Incredible lifted up the lorry and carried it to a garage for repairs. "Wow, Mr. Incredible saved the day!" shouted the crowd.

④ The lorry driver was very grateful to Mr. Incredible but there was another problem. "Without my lorry I won't be able to make my deliveries!" said the driver.

5 "Don't worry, I can help with that, too," Mr. Incredible replied. He quickly lifted the heavy boxes out of the lorry and began to deliver the goods.

6 His first delivery was a new television for a family. "Wow!" they cried. They couldn't believe that Mr. Incredible had delivered it to their house!

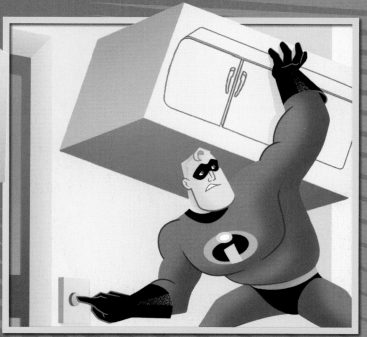

7 One lady had ordered both a new washing machine and a microwave. Mr. Incredible didn't mind. He could carry ten washing machines and ten microwaves!

8 By the end of the day, though, Mr. Incredible was very hot and tired from all the exercise. "Phew, only a freezer left to deliver!" he sighed.

9 "I should have guessed the freezer would be for you!" laughed Mr. Incredible, when he realised the last delivery was for his friend, Frozone!

10 "I'm really hot from all the lifting," Mr. Incredible said. "An ice cream will cool you down, my man," Frozone promised. "I'll make sure it's Super-chilled!"

The end

About the story

1 What had broken down?

2 Who lifted up the lorry?

3 What did Mr. Incredible deliver to the family?

4 Who was the last delivery for?

The chase

Dash is having fun escaping these Velocipods!
How many Velocipods are chasing him?

I counted ☐ Velocipods.

Answer: 9 Velocipods.

59

Super colours

Make Violet appear by tracing over the blue lines and then add some Super colours!

What colour is the guard's visor? Colour the box the same colour.

Answer: blue.

A helping hand

Mr. Incredible is hurrying home. Can you lead him to his family, lending a helping hand five times on the way?

Start

Finish

A busy night

1 One evening, La Ratatouille was even busier than usual. Hungry customers filled every table and more people were arriving by the minute!

2 "There's a queue of people outside waiting for tables!" Linguini told Remy, happily. The restaurant was becoming more and more popular.

3 In the kitchen, Remy was rushed off his little feet, trying to keep up with all the orders. "I think this is our busiest night, ever," Colette said, as she helped him.

4 By the end of the evening, Remy was tired from working so hard. "A busy chef deserves a quick nap," Colette told the little chef and so he closed his eyes.

5 Remy was enjoying a delicious dream about baking cakes, when Linguini suddenly woke him up. "There's still work to be done!" Linguini told him.

6 Remy was confused, because all the customers had gone home! He looked out at the dining area, just to make sure there was no-one left to serve.

7 "Not out there, Little Chef," Linguini laughed. "In here!" Remy watched as Linguini began to fill the kitchen sink with water and soapy bubbles.

8 "I'll wash and you can dry," Linguini told Remy. "I need to think of a recipe for edible plates," thought Remy, as he reached for the first plate.

The end

Berry cake

Remy is decorating a cake! Can you work out which colour comes next in each row? Finish off the patterns by colouring the last berries.

Add some colour to the strawberry before Remy adds it to the cake!

1

2

3

Answers: 1 – purple, 2 – red, 3 – red.

Cheese, please!

Remy needs three special cheeses for a recipe. Using his list, can you help him find them all?

1	The cheese with nuts on the top.	☐
2	The cheese with the most holes.	☐
3	The cheese that's red on the outside.	☐

Answers: 1 - c, 2 - b, 3 - e.

65

All aboard

Help Remy to answer these questions before the rat colony floats away!

1 Which two rats in this boat look the same?

2 Can you put the rushes in height order, starting with the shortest?

3 What is Remy using as a raft?

Answers: 1) the two black rats, 2) b, a, c, d, 3) a book, 4) the middle boat, 5) a cat.

4 Which boat is carrying the most rats?

5 Colour in the dotted sections to see what is hiding in the bin!

6 Can you spot four spoons in the scene? Colour a spoon each time you spot one.

Happy colours

Remy and Emile are happy because they've found a tasty snack! Can you add some cheesy colours?

What food have Remy and Emile found? Tick the correct box.

☐ or ☐

Answer: cheese.